TIME *for* TEA

A BOOK OF DAYS
—— *Compiled by* ——
JANE PETTIGREW

A Bulfinch Press Book
Little, Brown and Company
Boston · Toronto · London

First Edition

ISBN 0–8212–1830–1
A CIP catalogue record for this book
is available from the British Library.

Designed by The Image
Typeset by DP Photosetting, Aylesbury, Bucks

Published simultaneously in the United States of
America by Bulfinch Press, an imprint and
trademark of Little, Brown and Company (Inc.),
in Great Britain by Little, Brown and Company (UK) Ltd
and in Canada by Little, Brown & Company (Canada) Limited.

PRINTED IN SPAIN

INTRODUCTION

The story of tea is a fascinating one. It weaves its way through many countries and many centuries from the early days in China to its place today as Britain's national beverage. Few people are aware, when they boil a kettle and brew a quick "cuppa", that the history of tea and tea drinking has been intertwined with British history since the mid 1600s, and that its popularity in China and Japan goes back much further than that.

Various legends tell of the discovery of tea, the Indian and Japanese stories both attributing it to Bodhidharma, the devout Buddhist priest who founded Zen Buddhism. The Indian legend tells how the priest was in the fifth year of a seven-year, sleepless contemplation of Buddha when he began to feel drowsy. He quickly plucked a few leaves from a nearby bush and chewed them, immediately dispelling his sleepiness. The bush was, of course, a wild tea-tree. The Japanese version has it that he was so angry with his eyes for closing in sleep that he sliced off the eyelids and cast them to the ground. Where they fell, a bush grew, producing leaves that had the effect of increasing alertness and restoring energy. In the Chinese legend, the Emperor Shen Nung, a scholar and herbalist, was boiling his drinking water one day when he noticed that a few leaves had fallen into the pot from an overhanging tree. He was aware of a pleasant and appetizing smell wafting from the pot and, when he drank the liquid, found it to have restorative powers. In the story, Shen Nung's herbal experiment dates back to 2750 BC, but

Blue Cross recommended their tea as a first-aid measure that would revive and refresh.

the first references to tea do not appear until about the fourth century AD.

In each country where tea has become an established and popular beverage, the liquor has been drunk initially for its medicinal properties,

Hornimans Speciality Teas.
A taste to suit your style.
Other fine teas in the Hornimans range:

Assam Richness and depth of | East Grey A fine tea, subtly | Lapsang Souchong China teas | Ceylon A frequently distinctive
flavour to stimulate the palate. | scented with essence of Bergamot | with a light, smoky flavour. | tea, with a fine bouquet.

Darjeeling
A delicate tea
enhanced by its elusive
muscatel flavour.

Hornimans's advertisement projects tea as an elegant drink to enjoy by a cosy fireside.

and not immediately as a refreshing indulgence. Indeed the early brew would have had a rather bitter taste, since only green leaves were at first used – the process of fermenting the leaves and producing black tea as we know it was not developed until about AD 650.

From China, tea was carried to Japan by Buddhist scholars in the ninth century AD, but until the late sixteenth century no European, apart from the odd explorer, had heard of tea.

The Portuguese and the Dutch were the first traders, transporting regular shipments of the new herb to the ports of France, Holland and the Baltic coast in 1610. Small amounts probably filtered through to Britain as a result of journeys made by merchants and members of the court, but there is no record of tea being sold in England before 1658. The name Tea derives from the Chinese word *T'e*, or *Tcha* in Cantonese. In its early days in Britain it was referred to as "tay" or "tee" (pronounced tay until about 1711), and cheap black tea was known as "bohea".

With the cargoes of tea arrived also teapots and bowls from China and Japan. The quality of the fine porcelain thrilled European potters, who spent the next hundred years trying to perfect the manufacture of a similar material. It was in the 1660s that the word "china" was first used to encompass all the plates, bowls, saucers, jars and dishes imported from the Orient.

When tea first arrived in Britain it was sold loose by apothecaries and general merchants, and as a beverage in the popular coffee-houses. Coffee had arrived a little earlier, and the coffee-houses were favourite meeting-places for gentlemen from all walks of life. Ladies, however, drank their tea in the privacy of the home. Through the seventeenth century the price of a pound of tea was extremely high, owing mainly to the fact that it was a rare commodity, and when Charles II imposed a heavy tax the price went even higher. Throughout the first eighty years of the eighteenth century the cost was beyond the means of an average working man and his family, but smuggling, adulteration of the leaves and a thriving black market provided a cheaper supply. After the closure of the coffee-houses in the early eighteenth century, public tea drinking took place in the pleasure gardens at Vauxhall, Edgware, Ranalagh and elsewhere. Whereas the coffee-houses had been frequented only by men, these gardens appealed to men, women and children from all classes.

By the middle of the eighteenth century, tea had replaced ale and gin as the drink of the masses and had become Britain's most popular drink. It was taken at almost any time of the day or evening, the upper classes enjoying the habit of serving elegant bowls of tea after evening dinner. At the beginning of the nineteenth century, the Duchess of Bedford is said to have been the first to serve afternoon tea with some light refreshment and thus to have started a trend that is still an integral feature of British life.

As the new mealtime became more popular, so porcelain manufacturers, silversmiths and cabinet-makers produced a vast range of tea equipage that included teapots, cosies, sugar-bowls, cream and milk jugs, slop-bowls, cups and saucers, spoons and spoon trays, sugar-tongs, teapot stands, caddies, caddy spoons, silver kettles and trivets, urns, cake plates, tea tables and teapoys.

London's first tea-shop opened in 1884 and the fashion for going out to tea continued through the late Victorian days of increased wealth, and the Edwardian heyday of elegant tea-rooms, Palm Court orchestras, tango tea dances and outings on bicycles to country tea-

A plain card advertisement for Co-operative tea.

gardens. After a decline in interest in the fifties and sixties, the ritual of the tea hour has made a come-back, and the revival in interest has led to the opening of new tea-shops. Tea companies are offering a wider range of teas than ever before; hotels and restaurants are again organizing tea dances; tea paraphernalia and pretty table-cloths have been rescued from dusty boxes in attics; and people are again enjoying the cup that stimulates and refreshes, relaxes and revives, comforts and cheers.

❧ J A N U A R Y ❧

1	
2	
3	
4	
5	
6	
7	

ALL THE TEA IN CHINA

The history of tea drinking in China before the fourth century AD is riddled with confusions, puzzles and legends, but historians generally agree that the first authentic references to the leaf occur between AD 232 and 300. The first infusions were made with unprocessed green leaves and were drunk as a medicine or a stimulant. Gradually, however, tea was drunk more and more for pleasure, and by about AD 650 farmers in most provinces were cultivating at least a few bushes. In AD 780 a group of merchants, eager to boost sales and interest, commissioned the writer, Lu Yu, to compose the *Ch'a Ching*, the world's first book of tea. Lu Yu gave precise instructions for the brewing and serving of the beverage in a ritualized ceremony that involved 24 special objects. In praise of the drink, he wrote that "tea tempers the spirit and harmonizes the mind; dispels lassitude and relieves fatigue; awakens thought and prevents drowsiness."

During the T'ang Dynasty of AD 618–907, only cake tea was used. The leaves were steamed, pressed into a mould and baked into solid cakes. These were then shredded and added to boiling water with such flavourings as dates, cloves, orange peel, ginger, rice, milk, salt and sometimes even onions. Later, during the Sang Dynasty of 960–1127, the leaves were ground to a fine powder and whisked into boiling water with a bamboo whisk.

In the early days of tea drinking in China, demand was met by stripping tea-trees that grew in the wild. By AD 650 plantations were being cultivated, and legend has it that monkeys were used to gather the crop from the top branches.

❄ JANUARY ❄

8	
9	
10	
11	
12	
13	
14	

CAMELLIA SINENSIS

The tea-plant, or Camellia Sinensis, is an evergreen which, if allowed to grow, can reach a height of 15–20 feet. It bears dark green, rather leathery leaves, and produces small white flowers. When cultivated for commercial production the tea bushes are allowed to grow for four years or more before any leaves are plucked, and the matured shrubs then have a life of up to fifty years. By constant pruning and shaping, the bush is encouraged to produce a constant growth of young shoots with their pointed buds. The young leaves, called the "flush", are picked by hand, and the golden rule for good quality tea is "two leaves and a bud". For ordinary tea, pickers take a bud, the first two new leaves and the old leaf below them with the twig that joins them; for very fine tea, only the bud is nipped off. In some countries, where there is no cold season, the leaves are harvested all through the year at intervals of between seven and ten days. In countries where seasonal changes affect growth, the bushes must rest for part of the year and the harvests are referred to as first, second or third flush, and so on, each flush having its own characteristic quality and flavour. Other factors that determine the quality of the tea are the altitude at which the bushes are grown, the climate, the time of year and the size of leaf. A mature bush yields about one and a half pounds of tea a year.

The Camellia Sinensis produces sweet-smelling white flowers that look a little like a wild rose. The bush requires plenty of moisture and grows best in porous, loamy soil that is rich in humus.

Garraway's shop in Exchange Alley, between Lombard Street and Cornhill in the City of London, was the first shop to sell tea "in the leaf and drink", and also acted as an auction place for tea. Although it later dealt in other goods, the shop remained in business until 11 August 1866.

THE EXCELLENT CHINA DRINK

The first reference to tea in Europe was made in 1559 by a Venetian, Giambattista Ramusio, in a collection of travellers' tales. Over the following few years explorers, merchants and sailors brought back stories of tea drinking in China. By the late 1500s, the Portuguese and Dutch had both established trading posts in the Orient, and by the early 1600s were transporting regular cargoes of tea. But it was not until 1658 that the first British advertisement appeared in the September 23rd–30th edition of the weekly *Mercurius Politicus*, offering "that excellent China drink". In 1660, Thomas Garraway (or Garway, as he often called himself), merchant and proprietor of a coffee-house in the City of London, published a lengthy broadsheet entitled "An Exact Description of the Growth, Quality and Vertues of the Leaf Tea", which claimed that it would cure, among other ailments, headache, dropsy, scurvy, sleepiness, loss of memory, looseness of the guts, heavy dreams, and collick proceeding from the wind, and he assured readers that "if you are of corpulant body it ensures a good appetite, and if you have had a surfeit it is just the thing to give you a gentle vomit."

❄ JANUARY ❄

15

16

17

18

19

20

21

❧ JANUARY ❧

22

23

24

25

26

27

28

THE FASHIONABLE COFFEE-HOUSE

Coffee had arrived in Europe a little earlier than tea, and by the 1650s the coffee-house was an established part of London life. The first had opened in Oxford, and similar houses in Cambridge and London became very fashionable as meeting-places for business and relaxation. Each attracted a particular clientele – bankers, poets, stockbrokers, politicians – and the company of Lloyds shipping underwriters had its origins at Edward Lloyd's establishment.

These houses were the only places selling tea to drink (although loose tea was stocked by apothecaries), but they were exclusively for gentlemen, and ladies drank tea in the privacy of their homes. Other drinks served included ale, wine, rum punch, brandy, sherbet, coffee and chocolate – another new indulgence. Admission was one penny, a cup of tea or coffee cost two-pence, chocolate was a halfpenny dearer, and newspapers were free. The houses were often referred to as penny universities because of the discussion and conversation they encouraged. Indeed, they were such popular centres of academic, literary and political debate that some members of the government were afraid of their influence and persuaded King Charles to close them down. The royal proclamation caused such an outcry that it was withdrawn only eleven days later.

Tipping originated in the coffee-houses, where a box was nailed to the wall to receive money paid by customers "to insure promptness". By 1700 there were 2,500 coffee-houses in London, but during the early part of the eighteenth century they began to attract people of ill-repute and were closed down.

In the seventeenth and eighteenth centuries, tea was drunk in the morning and in the evening after dinner as well as during the day.

A CUPP OF TEE FOR MR PEPYS

Samuel Pepys recorded in his diary for 25 September 1660 that in the middle of a very busy day he "did send for a cupp of tee (a China drink) of which I had never drank before." Seven years later, his entry for 28 June 1667 shows that tea was still considered to be a medicine as well as a pleasurable refreshment. He wrote that he arrived "home and found my wife making of tea, a drink Mr Pelling, the potticary, tells her is good for her cold and defluxions."

Boswell's *Life of Johnson* also makes many references to tea drinking. Samuel Johnson described himself as a shameless tea drinker who "with tea amuses the evening, with tea solaces the midnight, and with tea welcomes the morning." It was perfectly normal for him to drink sixteen cups in very quick succession, and Boswell wrote, "I suppose no person ever enjoyed with more relish the infusion of that fragrant leaf than did Johnson." But not everybody was in favour. John Wesley was an ardent campaigner against the drink, professing that it caused "some symptoms of a Paralytick disorder". Jonas Hanway, another anti-tea activist, wrote in his *Essay on Tea* that it was robbing the people of their health and the nation of its wealth.

JAN • FEB

29
30
31
1
2
3
4

❧ FEBRUARY ❧

5

6

7

8

9

10

11

THE MYSTERIOUS LEAF

The work of plucking the tea-leaves is still done by hand, since fingers are the best tool for gathering the delicate young shoots. But the process that takes place in the plantation factory has gradually been mechanized. First the leaves are spread out in warm, dry air to wither them and reduce their moisture content. Next the leaves are gently rolled and slightly twisted to break the cells and release the natural juices. The leaves are then left in cool, humid air for about three hours to ferment (or oxidize) at the end of which they have changed to a bright, coppery colour. They are then fired by being passed slowly through hot chambers, where they darken and acquire the familiar, slightly burnt aroma of black tea. (Green tea is made by arresting the process after the initial withering so that no fermentation takes place. Oolong, which is only made from China tea, is semi-fermented and often scented with jasmine flowers, rose petals or lemon or orange blossom.) At the end of the process the tea is sorted according to grade and packed into foil-lined plywood chests. The two main grades are whole leaf and broken leaf, with several sub-divisions within each category.

Tea being packed tightly into chests on a Chinese plantation, long before the days of mechanization. The leaves were dried in the sun, crushed and rolled by hand, oxidised in the shade, rolled again and heated over a slow fire.

TEA IN THE GARDENS

During the eighteenth century tea-gardens became very fashionable in London and took the place of the coffee-houses. The idea was to provide tea and other refreshments in pleasant surroundings where people from all classes and all walks of life could enjoy a variety of entertainments. The four largest gardens were Vauxhall, Ranalagh, Cuper's Garden and Marylebone, and these were all patronized by royalty. They were open three or four days a week from April or May to September, and the admittance charge was usually one shilling, while Ranalagh charged half-a-crown, which included tea or coffee and bread and butter. Tea drinking was one of the main attractions, but the gardens all depended for their popularity on evening concerts, horse-riding, promenades, boat trips, illuminations, gambling, bowling greens, ballrooms with orchestras and secluded arbours where courting couples could find a little privacy. Bermondsey Spa and Saddler's Wells offered health-giving waters; Vauxhall was noted for its illuminations and concerts of music by Haydn and Corelli, Marylebone for its statue-lined walks, masked carnivals and firework displays; and Cuper's, (also known as Cupid's Garden) had written of it: "Tea and wine, here you may have, and also dine / But as you through the garden rove / Beware, fond youths, the darts of love." In America tea drinking was by

Emma Hart, née Lyon, was known as "the fair tea-maker of Edgware" during the days when she lived in Edgware Row as the mistress of Charles Greville, the famous diarist. As the lady of the house, she blended and served tea to Greville's guests, and when his uncle, Sir William Hamilton, met Emma, he quickly succumbed to her beauty and charm, and he would appear daily at the house to take tea. Not long afterwards, Emma married him and became Lady Hamilton. On one occasion during Emma's time with Charles Greville, she scandalized him at Ranalagh Gardens by singing to the public while her lover, thinking he had tucked her away safely in a private booth, went to make arrangements for their supper.

WHITE CONDUIT HOUSE

White Conduit Tea Garden stood in hayfields to the north west of London and enjoyed very good views towards Highgate and Hampstead. Cricket matches were regularly played there, the bats and balls being provided by the proprietor. The accepted technique at White's for a gentleman wishing to make a lady's acquaintance was to tread on the train of her dress, apologize profusely and then offer tea in one of the arbours.

this time as fashionable as in England, and several tea-gardens with very similar names opened in New York.

The rapid growth of London in the early nineteenth century led to the closure of the gardens, and thereafter the only place to drink tea was at home.

"A Tea Garden"
(The painting is by George Morland and is of Bragnigge Wells. The following inscription went with it)

All innocent within the shade you see
This little party sip salubrious Tea,
Soft Tittle-Tattle rises from the stream
Sweeten'd each word with Sugar and
    with Cream

Robert Sayer, February 1788

Even after the British potteries discovered how to manufacture porcelain, teacups were often still made in the traditional Chinese form, with no handles. Designs for teacup decoration were sent to China, and some Chinese porcelain was decorated at the English potteries. Early saucers were much deeper than today's, and held about the same amount of tea as the cup.

THE POTTER'S WHEEL

During the early days of tea drinking in Britain, teapots and cups were imported from China. Some of these were made of red-brown stoneware and some of translucent, hard, glazed porcelain, known as "china" by the British. The early pots were not teapots at all, but wine jars, and the Chinese and Japanese used them to hold the boiling water that was poured on to the leaves in small bowls. In Europe these handleless, saucerless bowls evolved into teacups, the idea of the handle being adapted from the English posset cup that was used for mulled ales and wines.

The tea ware was often shipped home by sailors and ships' officers who had bartered for them with the Chinese in exchange for iron and silver bars. Despite broken, missing or unmatching pieces, the porcelain was sold in Europe at between two and four times their price in Canton.

✳ FEBRUARY ✳

12

13

14

15

16

17

18

❄ F E B R U A R Y ❄

19
20
21
22
23
24
25

SILVER TEA WARE

English and American silversmiths have over the years produced some exquisite tea ware. The first known silver teapot was presented to the Committee of "ye East India Company" by Lord Berkeley in 1670. Silver teapots were not manufactured in quantity until the reign of Queen Anne (1706–1714). A heavy tax on silver, imposed at the end of the eighteenth century by William Pitt, made silver tea ware too expensive for many people, and as the British potteries expanded their trade, so porcelain began to take over from silver. But caddies, caddy spoons, teaspoons, spoon trays, kettles, trivets to support kettles or pots, trays, urns, slop-jars, sugar-bowls, cream jugs and mote skimmers were standard products of most silversmiths in the late seventeenth and early eighteenth centuries. The perforated mote skimmer or mote spoon (see below), was used to transfer tea-leaves from caddy to teapot, and to skim off any tea-leaves that escaped into the cup. The spike on the end was used to unblock the teapot spout when it became clogged with tea leaves.

As it became fashionable to take milk or cream in tea in the middle of the eighteenth century, one of the most popular shapes for the jug was that of a dairy cow. Although difficult to clean and therefore impractical, it continued to be very popular until Edwardian times.

TOM'S COFFEE HOUSE

In 1706, Thomas Twining opened "Tom's Coffee House" in Devereux Court, Temple Bar, just outside the City of London. The new venture was an immediate success, since it was set away from other coffee-houses and was ideally placed for barristers and attorneys from the nearby law courts; the shop specialized in selling loose tea and had many distinguished customers, and the company acted as a wholesaler to other retailers. In 1717, Thomas opened a separate tea and coffee warehouse next door to the coffee-shop and named it The Golden Lion.

"Tom's" was the first coffee-house into which a lady could venture to buy her tea. In the past she would have sent in her footman or coachman to make the purchase, for no lady would have dreamed of going inside. Today, the ninth generation of Twinings is still doing business at 216, The Strand.

FEB ◆ MARCH

26
27
28/29
1
2
3
4

❧ M A R C H ❧

5

6

7

8

9

10

11

UNSCRUPULOUS TRADERS

When Charles II needed to raise money in the second half of the seventeenth century, he imposed a hefty tax on certain drinks served in the coffee-houses. Duty on tea, coffee and chocolate was assessed at eightpence a gallon, and this was raised to two shillings in 1670. By 1689 even the cheapest tea cost seven shillings a pound – almost an entire week's wages for a labourer – and, since everyone was determined to continue drinking the, by now, very popular beverage, a healthy black market kept the supply going. Tea was smuggled in by ship, to be stored and distributed by a carefully organized network that involved farmhands, shopkeepers and even local parsons and politicians. To increase profits, some traders adulterated the tea with dry sloe and liquorice leaves, with used tea-leaves that had been stained with molasses and clay, or with ash leaves that had been dried and steeped in sheep's dung.

Black market Fine Hyson tea would have cost anything up to 36 shillings a pound. The name is said to come from the joining of two Chinese words Hsi Ch'un meaning "Joyous Spring". This was the name of a lady who improved the method of sorting her father's tea, whereupon, as his business vastly increased, he decided to name the tea after her.

LIFTING THE TAX

In 1725 a law was passed to fine tea smugglers and unscrupulous traders a sum of £100. In 1730 the fine was changed to £10 a pound, and in 1766 the penalty of imprisonment was added. In 1784 Richard Twining, who had always played a prominent role in protecting the good reputation of the tea trade, led a campaign to wipe out illegal tea trading. He exposed the illegal manufacture of adulterated tea (smouch, as he called it) and persuaded his fellow tea dealers not to bid at the East India Company's auctions, since that company was responsible for offering for sale "a considerable quantity of Tea which is either barely sweet, musty, or musty and mouldy". Twining realized that it was the high tax that was encouraging the black market, and he managed to convince Parliament that if they cut the tax, more tea would be sold and more revenue collected, even though the rate was lower. The tax was reduced from 119% to $12\frac{1}{2}$%, a rate of $2\frac{1}{2}$d per pound, and sales of tea leapt from five million pounds in 1784 to thirteen million in 1785.

William Pitt addresses the crowds on his reduction of the tea tax. In its place he imposed a window tax and a tax on coal and candles.

MARCH

12

13

14

15

16

17

18

✠ M A R C H ✠

19	
20	
21	
22	
23	
24	
25	

THE BOSTON TEA PARTY

When the British Parliament needed to raise money, particularly in times of war, tea was one of the commodities that were taxed, and the taxes were imposed on the American colonies as well as on the British. By the mid-eighteenth century, tea drinking in America was as widespread as it was in Britain, and the 1765 Stamp Act and the 1767 Act of Trade and Revenue were deeply resented, as many Americans disputed the right of Parliament to levy taxes on the colonies. The tax imposed was only threepence a pound, but the colonists refused to pay it and instead imported smuggled tea from Holland. The East India Company faced a huge drop in trade and persuaded the Government to pass the Tea Act of 1773, which gave them the right to export tea direct from the East to America. Although the price of tea therefore dropped, it still included a threepenny tax, and the colonists were furious. Agreements were signed not to accept the import of British goods, in particular tea, and some British captains supported the embargo. When three ships arrived in Boston harbour in December 1773, a band of men, disguised as American Indians, boarded the vessels and tipped £10,000 worth of tea into the harbour. Other "tea parties" followed elsewhere, and so began the rebellions that led to the War of Independence.

Although engravings show the men involved in the Boston affair elaborately dressed as Indians, most had only a daub of paint and an old blanket round their shoulders. For three hours they split open the chests with hatchets and tipped the tea into the harbour. As the water was shallow, tea piled up and was washed ashore in great banks the next morning.

☀MARCH ◆ APRIL☀

26	
27	
28	
29	
30	
31	
1	

TEA À LA MODE

The French and Germans became aware of tea at about the same time as the Dutch and Portuguese in the early 17th century. In Germany the only areas where tea was preferred to beer and coffee were in East Friesland and around Bremen. In France a fierce debate raged as to the value and expense of drinking tea. Physicians united in a campaign against it, but the aristocracy were very much in favour and drank it as an exotic, medicinal herb. Cardinal Mazarin took it for his gout, Racine drank it every day for breakfast, and Madame de Sévigné wrote of a sick friend who took it with milk. But as tea became more and more popular, so it lost its appeal to the French, and by 1700 they had turned instead to coffee and chocolate. Merchants realized that the only growing markets were Holland, England, Russia and America. In Russia, tea became popular at the court of the Romanovs, and by 1796 six thousand camel loads were being consumed annually. In America the taste for tea had been imported with the colonists, and the Quakers of Philadelphia created a large market for "the cups that cheer but do not inebriate". Had it not been for the Boston Tea Party, the Americans would no doubt have gone on drinking as much tea as the British.

Although by 1766 tea was no longer the preferred beverage in France, the nobility occasionally gave English-style tea-parties for special occasions, such as this visit by Mozart to the court of Prince Conti.

In 1751 the Worcester Tonquin company was established by fifteen English potters and, like other potteries, was soon producing small amounts of porcelain. Most factories concentrated on tea, coffee and chocolate services, since large flat dishes and plates tended to warp in the kiln.

THE SECRET OF PORCELAIN

The Chinese were reluctant to reveal the secret of how they made porcelain, and although the European potters strove to produce something similar, the best they achieved was at first a sort of earthenware coated with an opaque, enamel-like glaze, and, a little later, an unglazed stoneware similar to the Chinese ware but of inferior quality. A soft-paste porcelain was invented in France, but it was not until 1709 that real hard-paste porcelain was produced. Two Germans, Böttger and von Tschirnhausen, discovered that the missing ingredients were kaolin clay (or china clay) and so-called china stone – a silica and alumina stone that gives porcelain its translucency.

Europe's first china factory was established at Meissen in 1713, and, with the financial support of royalty and the nobility, the French and German potters could afford to experiment with the new formula. In England, the potteries depended on commercial success and could not afford to risk money trying out new methods, and so most factories continued to produce the safe stoneware and earthenware. However, some enterprising manufacturers started to experiment with porcelain, on a very small scale at first, and then, when wealthy clients proved that they were prepared to pay large sums for prestigious, good quality tableware, companies such as Worcester and Minton became very successful.

APRIL

2

3

4

5

6

7

8

☀ APRIL ☀

9
10
11
12
13
14
15

THE *SUKIYA* (OR TEA-HOUSE)

It was a Japanese Buddhist, returning from a period of study in China, who first took tea seeds to Japan. As soon as the first bushes were matured and ready for plucking, the Emperor Saga tried some tea, liked it and immediately ordered bushes to be cultivated in five provinces. In Japan, as elsewhere, tea was taken as a remedy at first, but gradually it became, in the words of Okakuraj Kakuzo in his *Book of Tea*, "an idealization of the form of drinking; it is a religion of the art of life". He also wrote, "The tea-room was an oasis in the dreary waste of existence where weary travellers could meet to drink from the common spring of art-appreciation."

The tea ceremony is a direct development of Zen Buddhist rituals, and there is also a strong Taoist influence. The guests arrive and wait for their host in the waiting room or forecourt. They are then led to the tea-room, stopping on the way to wash at a stone basin. The *cha-shitsu* (tea-room) is decorated with a scroll and fresh flowers. Thick tea is served initially, followed by thin whipped tea. The bowl of tea is passed around and small morsels of food are offered. Drinking and eating are followed by conversation, and guests then move to another room, where more thin tea is served. Now individual bowls are used, and the atmosphere is more relaxed and informal. The whole ceremony takes about four hours.

The traditional Japanese tea-house (*sukiya*, meaning "abode of fancy") consists
of a waiting-room (*yoritsuki*), a preparation room (*mizu-ya*) and a tea-room
(*cha-shitsu*). A garden path (*roji*) leads to the entrance.

✄ A P R I L ✄

16

| 17 |

| 18 |

| 19 |

| 20 |

| 21 |

| 22 |

THE DUCHESS SETS A NEW TREND

The very English ritual of taking afternoon tea is thought to have been invented by Anna, the 7th Duchess of Bedford, in the early nineteenth century. Breakfast in those days was at nine or ten o'clock in the morning and, during the eighteenth century, the hour for dinner had gradually changed from three or four o'clock in the afternoon to seven or eight in the evening, lunch being a light, informal meal. Consequently, the Duchess found that she grew a little peckish at about four o'clock, and one day she asked her maid to bring a pot of tea and some light refreshment to her room. She was so delighted with the arrangement that she soon invited her friends to join her, and, in no time at all, afternoon tea-parties were absolutely the thing to do.

Fine porcelain tea ware was arranged on silver trays or occasional tables, and dainty sandwiches, cakes and biscuits were set out invitingly on silver dishes. The lady of the house would brew the tea, measuring the leaves from a locked ornate caddy that was kept in the drawing-room or salon, since tea was too expensive to be left with the servants. When the tea had been carefully brewed, footmen, parlourmaids or any gentlemen friends present would serve the tea and hand round the sandwiches and cakes.

As the fashion for afternoon tea caught on, tea equipage developed into the complete service that we know today – teapot and stand, sugar-bowl, milk jug or creamer, slop-bowl, teacups and saucers, teaspoons and spoon tray, sugar-tongs, and cake plates for displaying savoury and sweet foods.

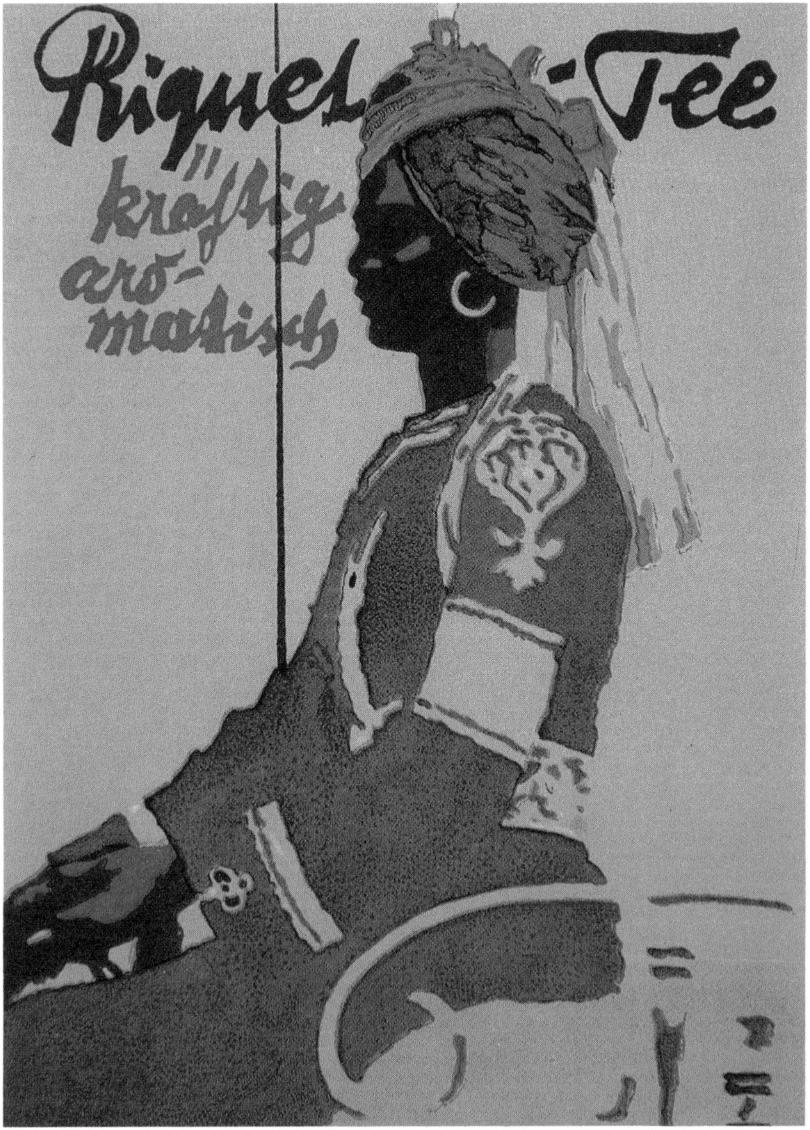
Riquet -Tee
"kräftig
aro-
matisch

TEA FROM INDIA

Until 1838 all the tea imported to Britain came from China. For a long time the English had wanted to grow tea in India, but plants from China had not thrived in Indian soil. In 1823 Charles and Robert Bruce discovered indigenous Indian tea-trees and sent specimen plants and seeds to the Botanic Gardens in Calcutta.

In 1833 the East India Company lost its monopoly of the tea trade with China, and it was decided that the company would try to establish plantations in India. They persisted in trying to grow the Chinese plants, and chose totally unsuitable sites. At last the Bruce brothers convinced the company that Upper Assam was already a vast area of tea country, and cultivation began. Although the Chinese plants were still favoured, native Indian bushes soon replaced them and the first shipment of eight chests of Assam tea arrived in London in 1838. The Assam Tea Company was formed in 1840, and Charles Bruce was put in charge of the northern division. Local workers were hard to find, so labour was imported from Singapore. In 1839 the province of Assam was annexed to the British crown, but tea growing was left in the hands of the privately owned Assam Company. The company expanded later into Darjeeling, Cachar, Sylhet and other North Indian areas. The company declared its first earned dividend in 1852.

APRIL

23

24

25

26

27

28

29

APRIL • MAY

30

1

2

3

4

5

6

THE AGE OF THE CLIPPER

Until the 1840s the ships of the East India Company took between twelve and fifteen months to sail from China to London. They carried huge cargoes but their weight slowed them down. In 1845 the first American clipper ship was launched and made the round trip from New York in less than eight months. British ship owners realized the threat this posed to trade, and in 1850 the first British clipper, *The Stornaway*, was built in Aberdeen. Some British owners had ships built in America, and one of these, *The Lightning*, logged an average speed of eighteen knots, a record for sailing ships.

The clippers were built like sleek yachts, with elaborate decoration and graceful lines, but they were also capable of carrying more than a million pounds of tea. The chests were intricately packed by experienced and skilled Chinese stevedores, who managed almost to mould the cargo to the curve of the ship, each tier of chests, beaten into place with wooden mallets, looking like an even planked deck. The solidity of the stowage helped to increase the ship's strength and performance, so that it could withstand the onslaught of the monsoons, fast currents, gales and reefs as well as the pirate ships that endangered every voyage. Some ships took risks in order to save time, and were wrecked, but most reached port safely.

For a long time Fouchow had been one of the major Chinese ports, being relatively close to the main growing areas of Canton. As soon as ships had finished loading, they rapidly set off for London, sometimes not even stopping to complete the necessary paperwork for fear of losing the race to ships that had already set sail.

UNDER FULL SAIL

British Navigation Laws debarred non-British ships from entering British ports and owing to the resulting lack of competition, British companies were not concerned with the speed of delivery from China to the London docks. However, when the laws were repealed in 1849, the new, very fast American clippers posed a threat, and the idea of racing the cargo home began.

As soon as the tea-chests were stowed, the clippers set sail, usually in June, but sometimes as early as May. The arrival in London was usually in October, but the greatest race of all, in 1866, finished with a dead heat between the *Ariel* and the *Taeping* on 7 September. The winner of any race was decided when the first tea-chest was landed on the wharf, and in this case the owners decided to share the prize – an extra ten shillings per ton of tea.

With the advent of steamships and the opening of the Suez Canal in 1869, the clippers were doomed, but some continued through the 1870s and 80s, carrying wool and emigrants to New Zealand and Australia.

Once the ships arrived in the London docks, the tea-chests were unloaded by dock workers and crew (which often included a number of Chinese), and brokers immediately took samples.

MAY

7	
8	
9	
10	
11	
12	
13	

✂ M A Y ✂

14

15

16

17

18

19

20

TEA-TIME TREATS

A typical afternoon tea in the Duchess of Bedford's day would have consisted of tea, blended by the Duchess herself in front of her guests, and platefuls of dainty refreshments: neat sandwiches, biscuits such as shortbread and macaroons, light cakes, for example madeira, rice cake or seed cake, and little cakes such as queen cakes or maids of honour. In winter there would be more substantial treats: muffins, tea cakes and Sally Lunns would be served, and the cakes would be heavier – pound cake and gingerbreads were particularly popular.

Later in the century, Mrs Beeton, the household management expert, gave instructions for serving an "At Home Tea", at which a lady received several of her friends. She advised that the tea be served "upon small tables, the servant before bringing it in, seeing that one is placed conveniently near her mistress, who generally dispenses the tea. . . . Thin bread and butter, cake and sometimes fresh fruit are all the eatables given."

The cake may be decorated by sprinkling it with caster sugar and garnishing it with strips of angelica and half glacé cherries, or it may be covered with lemon water icing and garnished in the same way.

MADEIRA CAKE

This very popular cake is a traditional accompaniment to afternoon tea, and there are many different methods of making it. This recipe comes from Eliza Acton's Modern Cookery, *published in 1845, forty years or so after the invention of the meal by the Duchess of Bedford.*

Before mixing the cake, heat the oven to gas 4/350°F/180°C and grease and line a 7-inch round tin.

"Whisk four eggs until they are as light as possible, then, continuing still to whisk them, throw in by slow degrees the following ingredients in the order in which they are written: six ounces of dry, pounded and sifted sugar; six of flour, also dried and sifted; four ounces of butter, just dissolved, but not heated; the rind of a fresh lemon; and the instant before the cake is moulded, beat well in the third of a teaspoon of carbonate of soda; bake it an hour in a moderate oven. In this, as in all compositions of the same nature, observe particularly that each portion of butter must be beaten into the mixture until no appearance of it remains before the next is added; if this be done, and the preparation be kept light by constant whisking, the cake will be as good, if not better, than if the butter were creamed."

✠ M A Y ✠

21

22

23

24

25

26

27

TRADE MONOPOLY

On 31 December 1600, Queen Elizabeth chartered the East India Company for the "honour of the nation, the wealth of the people ... the increase of navigation and the advancement of lawfulle traffic." The company was granted a monopoly on all trade east of the Cape of Good Hope and west of Cape Horn. The East Indiamen, the company's ships, carried home tea, cloth (including silk), gold and chinaware. At first, the company had no established base in China, but imported from Macao and Bantam and by other indirect routes, but in 1700 they set up base at Canton. By 1830 the company still enjoyed its monopoly, despite efforts in London by competitors to change the position. This was mainly because the British government regarded the Chinese as difficult to deal with and, since they were receiving as much tea as they wanted, they saw no reason to alter the status quo. However, an unlikely factor caused the weakening of the East India Company's hold on the market – opium. Opium was the one commodity that the Chinese wanted from the British, for, although it was officially banned, it was widely used. The company was quite prepared to make money out of growing the drug in India, as long as it was not seen to be actually selling it in China. So intermediate companies became involved, and these were also able to infiltrate the tea trade.

Workers in the London docks were as skilled at unloading the tea as the Chinese stevedores were at loading it. Records show that after the *Fiery Cross* had tied up in St Katharine's Docks at 4 am on 20 September 1864, it only took the dockers until 10 am the following day to unload the cargo of fourteen thousand chests of tea.

✂ M A Y ◆ J U N E ✂

28

29

30

31

1

2

3

ON THE BOIL

Tea-kettles made their first appearance at the end of the seventeenth century. The task of brewing the tea was considered too skilled and important to be left to the servants, and it was always the responsibility of the lady of the house. The brewing was part of the tea ritual, and all the necessary equipment, including the kettle, appeared in the drawing-room, salon or library at the appointed hour.

Early kettles were made of silver, and resembled teapots in shape, often with an elegant swan-neck spout and a nob of ebony or stained black wood. The kettle had its own spirit burner and sat on a special table called a kettle stand. This was usually about thirty inches high, and had a lattice-work or galleried rim and a metal lining to protect the wood from the heat of the kettle.

The popularity of the kettle declined in the 1770s, when the urn became more fashionable. The most popular urns were shaped like vases and stood on an elegant stemmed foot. The water was kept hot by a red-hot cylindrical box-iron inserted into a silver cavity in the body of the urn, or by charcoal in the base.

An urn of boiling water sitting on or beside the tea table made the brewing of tea and the refreshing of the pot much easier. It was also safer than the earlier tea-kettle spirit burner, with its open flame.

The reader of leaves needs to be able to interpret strange and muddled formations in order to predict the future and analyse the past. Small dots of tea mean that money will be forthcoming, circles indicate the completion of some current ambition or project, while drops of tea signify sadness.

READING THE LEAVES

Tasseography is defined as an intuitive art with psychic skill which enables the reader to foretell the future. For those wishing to try it, the best results are obtained by using a loose Indian tea with fairly large leaves in a cup with no interior pattern. Pour off most of the tea and allow the leaves to settle. Swirl the dregs and then quickly invert the cup over the saucer. When the cup is turned back to its correct position, some of the wet leaves should be stuck to the inside of the cup. Some say that the cup should be swirled three times in a clockwise direction.

The leaves are traditionally "read" as follows: If there are a lot of leaves in the cup, the subject will have a full rich life and has a generous but slightly emotional character. Few leaves indicate a controlled, logical person who is somewhat cold and over-disciplined. Leaves deposited where the handle joins the cup refer to personal and home life; leaves to the left of the handle represent the past, and to the right, the future. Leaves in the bottom indicate bad luck, leaves near the rim refer to the present, and, near the bottom, the distant future. Letters, and certain other recognizable shapes and formations, tell the reader of specific influences and happenings.

A single leaf floating on a full cup of tea also means that money is on the way, and one leaf stuck at the side indicates news of the arrival of a stranger.

❀ JUNE ❀

| 4 |
| 5 |
| 6 |
| 7 |
| 8 |
| 9 |
| 10 |

❧ J U N E ❧

11	
12	
13	
14	
15	
16	
17	

TOTALLY TEETOTAL

The temperance reformers' involvement with tea stemmed from the inaugural meeting of the Church Missionary Society, in April 1799, at which tea was drunk and the teapot took pride of place. The *Oxford Dictionary* gives the date of the invention of the word teetotal (or t-total) as 1834, just as the temperance movement was at the height of its activities, and it is possible that the word has close connections with the beverage.

Tea meetings were held both to recruit reformed drinkers and abstainers and to raise money for the cause. In Preston in 1833 over one thousand tickets were sold for a meeting, and twelve hundred people sat down in relays while a two hundred gallon boiler prepared the water for the tea. Forty reformed drinkers acted as waiters and filled kettles for each table from huge tanks measuring three feet square and one foot deep. Men and women paid ninepence, youngsters sixpence, and the food was provided by local volunteers. However, the humorous portrayal by Dickens in his *Pickwick Papers* (1836) of people almost drowning themselves in tea at a meeting, led to a gradual decline in the popularity of such events. Dickens was not against tea, but he was against sanctimonious behaviour. He did, in fact, express the view that tea and coffee were necessary home comforts.

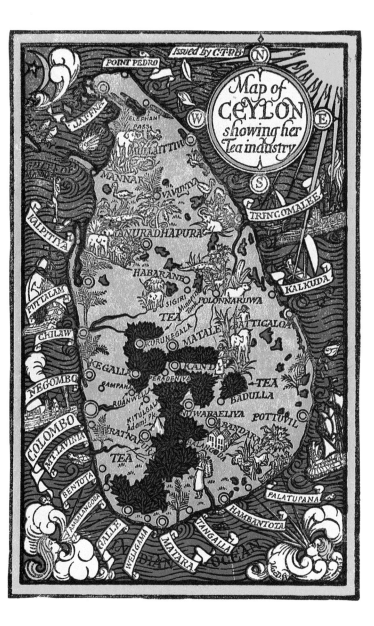

THE EMERALD OF THE EAST

The first commercially produced crop to be grown in Sri Lanka, or Ceylon as it was known then, was cinnamon. This was followed in the 1820s by coffee, but the entire coffee industry was wiped out by coffee rust. The next venture was the production of quinine, but the market collapsed. An excellent alternative was tea, and from about 1873 tea production expanded rapidly. It was the foresight of a newcomer that was to ensure that Ceylon tea became as popular in Britain as the Indian and China varieties.

Thomas Lipton, son of a Glaswegian grocer, had started his working life as a cabin boy. After several years of working in America, he returned to Glasgow to work in his parents' shop and to expand the business. Tea was still expensive, and Lipton realized that by producing his own tea and by cutting out the middle men, he could sell much more cheaply. In 1888 he bought several estates in Ceylon, and sold tea cheaper than all other retailers, campaigning with the slogan "Direct from the Tea Gardens to the Tea Pot".

Exports of tea from Ceylon rose from just 23 pounds in 1873 to 149,264,603 pounds in 1900. Tea from the low-lying areas has a strong, sometimes even coarse flavour, whereas tea from the cooler uplands gives a liquor that is fine and delicate.

JUNE

18

19

20

21

22

23

24

❧ JUNE ◆ JULY ❧

25	
26	
27	
28	
29	
30	
1	

PRESSURE TO BUY

By the middle of the eighteenth century, there was no need for the tea companies to sell the idea of tea to the British people – tea was by this time the national beverage – but they did need to find ways of encouraging customers to buy their tea rather than that of their competitors.

Twinings could use the fact that they were "suppliers to the nobility and gentry" to attract new clients, and Melrose built their reputation on a thriving business with "skilled artisans and keepers of furnished lodgings". Several companies used sugar as their loss-leader, while others offered free street maps or decorative almanacs. In 1872, the London Genuine Tea Company invited sub-postmasters to act as their agents, and postmen to sell teas from door to door. David Lewis, who made a feature of selling "Two-shilling Tea" in the centre of the ground floor of his department store in Birmingham, had a waltz song, "Lewis's Beautiful Tea", as his advertisement. By the end of the century, Liptons were selling cheap tea in their four hundred branches, and retailers were offering all sorts of gifts to tempt customers – teapots, pianos, babies' chairs, household linens, trays and cups and saucers, and even pensions were given free with varying amounts of tea or in return for labels from tea packets.

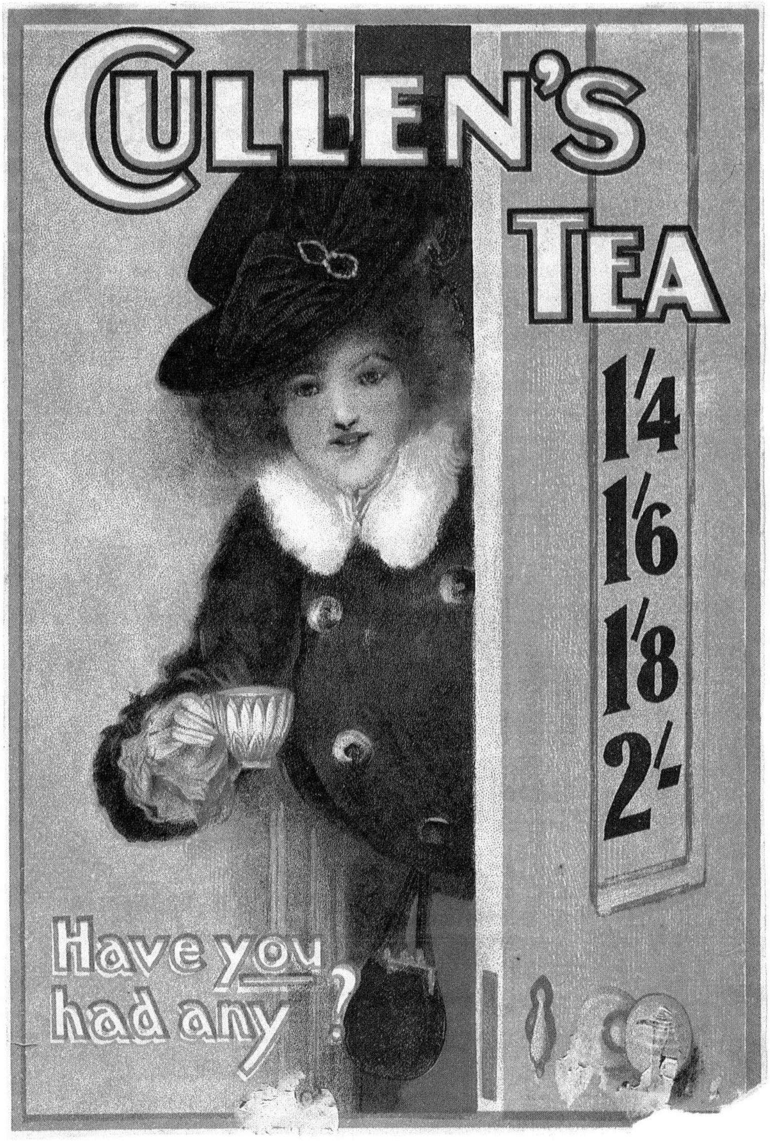
CULLEN'S
TEA
1/4
1/6
1/8
2/-
Have you
had any?

One of the ABC tea-shops in 1900. The ABC waitresses, noted for their prompt and professional service, were known as "nippies".

AS EASY AS ABC

The growth of London during the first half of the nineteenth century led to the closure of the tea-gardens, and until 1884 there was nowhere to go for tea. In that year, the manageress of the London Bridge branch of a chain of bakers – the Aerated Bread Company – was responsible for the opening of London's first tea-shop. This enterprising lady was in the habit of inviting her best customers into the back room of the shop for a cup of tea and a chat, and she hit on the idea of opening the area as a public tea-room. With the blessing of her directors, the ABC tea-shop opened and set a trend that was to be quickly followed by the Express Dairy, J. Lyons, which had originally been a tobacconist, Kardomah, a tea and coffee company of Liverpool, and several smaller companies that set up all over Britain.

The ABC and the Express Dairy provided reasonably priced refreshment, including meals, for modest middle- and working-class people. Lyons first Corner House had red silk on the walls, red plush chairs, gas-lit chandeliers and waitresses dressed in elegant floor-length grey uniforms. Most branches however, were fairly simple, functional places, equipped with serviceable marble-topped tables, scrubbable floors and bentwood chairs. In some, palm court orchestras provided the music for dancing.

JULY

2

3

4

5

6

7

8

The distinctive feature of MOORE BROS' System is that they supply FAMILIES DIRECT at MERCHANTS' PRICES for Cash £3 value, carriage paid.

TALES FROM CHINA

When the English porcelain companies started manufacturing tea ware, the designs were strongly influenced by Chinese patterns. Thomas Minton, who worked as a master graver in London before setting up his own pottery, is often credited with having engraved the first willow pattern for Josiah Spode's Staffordshire works in the 1780s. A number of other potteries copied the very successful design, and

it is still extremely popular today. It tells the legend of Koong-tse and Chang:

Koong-tse was the beautiful daughter of a rich man and lived with her father in the house that stands in the middle of the willow pattern. Behind the house is an orange tree; in front, a footbridge with a willow tree overhanging it. Koong-tse falls in love with her father's poor clerk, Chang.

This angers her father, who promptly dismisses Chang from his employ, quickly marries Koong-tse to an old but wealthy mandarin and builds a palisade to keep the young lovers apart. Koong-tse is restricted to the garden and tea-house, encircled by a stream, but Chang manages to float messages down the stream to her with plans for her escape. The three figures running down the footpath are Koong-tse, who is carrying a distaff (a symbol

Now CHIN-CHIN was a clever Man!
(Which comes from drinking TEA.)
For books he was mad,
And he always had
     Confucius
          on his
               Knee.

"A Daily Treat"
TOWER TEA

TOWER TEA LIMITED
LONDON

of purity), Chang, who carries a box of jewels given to Koong-tse by the mandarin, and the furious father, waving a whip. The little boat carries the lovers to an island in the upper left corner of the design, and here they build a house and take up farming. But Chang is also a successful writer, and eventually the old mandarin hears of his fame, tracks him down and has him killed. When Koong-tse commits suicide, the gods take pity on the two, transforming their souls into a pair of immortal doves, the emblems of constancy, that are seen flying above the design.

A Chinese mystic of the T'ang Dynasty wrote, "The first cup of tea moistens my lips and throat. The second shatters my loneliness. The third causes the wrongs of life to fade gently from my recollection. The fourth purifies my soul. The fifth lifts me to the realms of the unwinking gods."

CUCUMBER SANDWICHES

INGREDIENTS

1 large cucumber
creamed butter
white or brown bread
salad oil
lemon-juice or vinegar
salt and pepper.

Method – Peel the cucumber, slice it thinly, season liberally with salt, drain on a seive for about 1 hour, and dry thoroughly. Now put it into a basin and sprinkle with pepper, salad oil, lemon-juice, or vinegar, liberally or otherwise according to taste. Have ready some thin slices of bread and butter, stamp out some rounds of suitable size, place slices of cucumber between two rounds of bread, and press the parts well together. Dish lightly overlapping each other in a circle on a folded napkin, and serve garnished with parsley.
From *Mrs Beeton's Family Cookery*

Various editions of *Mrs Beeton's Book of Household Management*, originally published in 1861, give careful instructions for making sandwiches. She wrote: "The old, comparatively substantial form still accompanies the sportsman and traveller, but those intended for 'afternoon tea' are dainty trifles, pleasing the eye and palate, but too flimsy to allay hunger where it exists. . . . Sandwiches for afternoon tea, or any occasion where they will come into contact with gloved fingers, should be left perfectly plain on the outside. . .".

Ever since the early days of afternoon tea in Britain, dainty sandwiches have always been a popular form of light refreshment. The sandwich was invented in 1762 by John Montague, fourth Earl of Sandwich. Legend has it that he was an avid gambler, and while in the middle of one of his customary 24-hour sessions at the gaming table, asked his servant to bring him two slices of bread with a slice of beef between, so that he could eat without disturbing the game. The Earl's family have since said that it was not at the gaming table but at his desk at the Admiralty that the Earl needed such nourishment, since he led a very busy working life as Secretary of State and First Sea Lord, and often worked in his office for twelve hours or more at a time.

❧ JULY ❧

9

10

11

12

13

14

15

⚔ JULY ⚔

16

17

18

19

20

21

22

DO YOU TAKE SUGAR?

Sugar was first imported to Britain with other spices from the Orient during the reign of Henry III (1216–1272). The sugar arrived as flat blocks known as sugar cakes, which were broken into small pieces and crushed in a pestle and mortar into a coarse powder. This was called blanch-powder and was very expensive. The refining of sugar by washing and crystalizing into conical moulds was invented in Venice in the fifteenth century. This produced a much whiter sugar, but sugar-bakers were still known to improve its appearance with a coating of white lead as late as 1856.

The earliest sugar-bowls for use on the table date from Henry VIII's reign, when sugar was used to sweeten and smooth wine. Sugar in tea became popular in the late seventeenth century, when sugar-bowls, tongs and teaspoons became standard tea accessories. Sugar was purchased in tall, conical loaves weighing about six pounds. Lumps were broken off with a special chopper and cracked with sugar nippers rather like a pair of sharp pliers. Silver sugar-tongs were used at the tea table to transfer the small pieces from the bowl to the cup. Tongs were sometimes equipped with a sharp spike that was used, like the spike on a mote spoon, to unblock the spout of the teapot. Teaspoons were at first the same size as coffee spoons, but later became about twice the size.

By the middle of the nineteenth century, even dolls' tea-sets would have
included a sugar-bowl and tiny teaspoons. The bowl would have contained
lumps of "sugar royal", the best quality loaf sugar. Granulated sugar did not
become available until 1900.

TERRABONA TEAS AND COFFEES

Their Royal Highnesses the PRINCE and PRINCESS of WALES accepting Caskets of TERRABONA TEA & COFFEE at the Company's depot at Constantinople (Olympia) on February the 8th 1894

Princess Victoria of Wales

Princess Maud of Wales

Tea companies have always liked to give their blends of tea royal names, and over the years various royal persons have been used to decorate tea packets and caddies. Edward, Prince of Wales, was a favourite figure for, among others, Hornimans, Drysdales, Twinings and Terrabona.

A RIGHT ROYAL TEA

In 1662, tea drinking received the royal seal of approval when Charles II married Catherine of Braganza. As a member of the Portuguese royal family she was already an avid tea drinker and brought with her, as part of her dowry, a chest of tea. She quickly introduced her friends at court to the beverage and helped to establish a demand among the English aristocracy. On the first birthday that she celebrated in England, Edmund Waller wrote a poem to her in which he praised her – "The best of Queens" – for having made the English aware of the "best of herbs".

By the time Victoria came to the throne in 1837, the annual consumption of tea in Britain had increased from sixty-six thousand pounds in 1701 to nearly thirty million pounds. On hearing of her accession to the throne, the Queen is reported to have said, "Bring me a cup of tea and *The Times*."

Queen Mary, the wife of George V, was a great lover of afternoon tea. Charles Oliver writes in *Dinner at Buckingham Palace*: "Everything had to be fully ready at 4 pm punctually, with sandwiches, cakes and biscuits invitingly set out on gleaming silver dishes upon a smoothly-running trolley. The teapot, cream jug, hot water jug and sugar-bowls were always the same antique silver service which had been a favourite of Queen Victoria."

❧ JULY ❧

23

24

25

26

27

28

29

JULY • AUG

30	
31	
1	
2	
3	
4	
5	

THE FINE ART OF TAKING TEA

The smaller details of tea etiquette have varied greatly over the years. In the late seventeenth century, when a lady had sipped enough tea, she laid her spoon across the top of her cup, tapped the cup gently with the spoon, or turned the cup upside down, and one of the gentlemen present would remove it. In Edinburgh it was considered correct to leave the spoon upright in the cup after stirring, instead of laying it on the saucer. In eighteenth-century America, when ladies were invited to a tea-party, each took with her a small teacup and saucer of the finest porcelain and a spoon. Sugar in tea was already popular, and "Bite-and-Stir" boxes, divided into two compartments, held both powdered sugar for stirring into the tea and lump sugar. It was very fashionable to nibble a small piece of sugar and drink the tea through it.

The very newness of tea in the late seventeenth and early eighteenth centuries led to some strange occurrences. One lady from Penrith is said to have boiled a pound of leaves (worth a fortune in those days), thrown away the liquor and served her guests with platefuls of tea-leaves with butter and salt. Another served the liquid in cups and made little sandwiches with the leaves! In late Victorian and Edwardian days, it was perfectly acceptable to drink tea from the saucer.

A Tea Party – or English Manners – and French Politeness. —

A Frenchman not aware of the custom, constantly returned his Cup without the spoon in it – which being immediately replenished by the Lady of the house, he thought it a point of politeness to drink the contents which he continued to do, to the great surprise of the company until he perceived the Lady pouring out the 14th Cup, when he rose in great agony and cried Ah! Madame, excuse me I can take no more. ——

This Cruickshank cartoon highlights one of the problems experienced by those who did not understand the finer details of tea etiquette.

In summer, afternoon tea is often served in the garden, with delicate
sandwiches, strawberry tartlets and buttery shortbreads. In winter, when cosy
armchairs are drawn up to a blazing fire, tea is a comforting meal of toasted
crumpets, muffins and teacakes spread with honey or jam, and delicious cakes,
gingerbreads and pastries.

HIGH TEA AND LOW TEA

Because afternoon tea is taken at low tables that rest beside guests' armchairs, it was at one time also called low tea. It has traditionally been a very elegant meal, served on a table that is laid with a pretty cloth, with the best china or silver, and with very dainty food.

High tea, by contrast, is a hearty, filling, nourishing meal that originated during the Industrial Revolution of the nineteenth century. Workers were hungry when they returned home after a long, hard day in the factories, mines and workshops, and high tea was the main meal of the day. It has not changed very much from those days and consists of hot or cold savoury dishes such as pies, cold meat, Welsh rarebit and salads, followed by generous loaves of home-baked bread with cheeses, pickles and jams. Then come cakes – fruit loaves, fruit cakes, sponges, pastries and biscuits. It is still a popular meal in some parts of Britain and especially for families with school-age children who often need a homely, filling tea once the school day is over.

❈ AUGUST ❈

6
7
8
9
10
11
12

✴AUGUST✴

13

14

15

16

17

18

19

A TASTE FOR TEA

When tea arrives in Britain it is stored in its chests in special warehouses where it is weighed and marked. Brokers then taste the various teas before buying and selling them at auction. Professional tea tasters require years of training and experience before they can assess the different flavours and qualities. In the tasting room, an equal weight of each tea is brewed in a separate pot and allowed to infuse for five or six minutes. The liquid is then strained into a bowl and the leaves are tipped into the upturned lid of the pot. The taster then smells the infusion and, using a fairly large, silver or silver-plated spoon, sucks some of the tea on to the taste-buds of the tongue, savours the tea and then spits it out into a spittoon. The final assessment is made on the colour and quality of the dry leaf, the appearance of the infused leaves and the colour of the liquor.

Tea tasting goes on at the plantation, at the auction and on the premises of
the tea merchants. The technique has not changed very much in two centuries.
Each batch to be tasted must be identical in weight, brewed with an exact
volume of boiling water and infused for precisely the same length of time.

✺ AUGUST ✺

20	
21	
22	
23	
24	
25	
26	

NURSERY TEAS

In a late Victorian edition of *Mrs Beeton's Cookery Book* we read: "Except in the nursery or in large families, the old-fashioned 'tea' has ceased to exist. . . . We can only expect the ordinary 'at home' tea in tiny cups with its accompanying thin bread and butter. . . ."

Children of middle- and upper-class families in Victorian and Edwardian days often ate lunch with their parents and were expected to be on their best behaviour, but tea-time in the nursery was supervised by the nanny or nursery maid, and the meal was laid out in a room that was filled with favourite toys and books. The food was geared to the children's taste, and favourites were boiled eggs with soldier boy fingers of bread and butter, marmite sandwiches, banana sandwiches, scones, gingerbreads and jelly. *In Memories of Three Reigns* (published in 1873), Lady Raglan recalled some happy teas enjoyed as a child with friends in their schoolroom: "Everything was home-made, the bread and the cakes and the scones. And there was a particular delicacy associated with this place which I particularly loved. It was ginger jumbles, which were served all hot and crisp and sticky like treacle. . .".

A typical family tea in Victorian days consisted of sardines on toast, anchovy toast or potted meat, bread and butter or hot toast, jam, honey, cakes and sometimes fruit.

TANGO TEAS

The tango originated in the back streets of Buenos Aires and was first demonstrated in Paris before the craze hit London in 1912. Tango teas and matinées very quickly became the "in" thing; tango clubs were set up in hotels, restaurants and theatres, and dance teachers such as Victor Silvester (who started his career teaching the tango at Harrods tea dances) made their fortunes. One of the most exclusive clubs was at the Carlton Hotel. It met every Tuesday and Thursday from 4 o'clock to 6.30, and ". . . well-known people are seen on every side. The dancing enthusiasts come early, and spend the whole afternoon; others drop in for half-an-hour; while many of the members bring parties of young people who seem to enjoy the novelty of dancing in the afternoon and seldom leave until after the last bar of music has been played."

☒ A U G ◆ S E P ☒

27	
28	
29	
30	
31	
1	
2	

DRESSING FOR TEA

From mid-Victorian days onwards, British fashion designers delighted in creating special outfits in which to attend or give afternoon tea-parties. Towards the end of the century, loose, comfortable tea-gowns became very popular for wearing around the house on informal afternoons. These were often made of white cotton or linen, trimmed with white broderie anglaise, tucks and frills and, sometimes, coloured ribbons. As fashions changed, tea-gowns became shorter, although tango dance dresses were often ankle or lower calf length. In the 1930s smart ladies visiting friends for tea would often dress elegantly in stylish hats, and shoulder fox furs over crêpe or chiffon dresses. The trend for going out to tea dwindled in England during the 1950s and 60s, but today's revival of interest in tea dancing has set a new fashion for pretty afternoon dresses worn with hats and gloves.

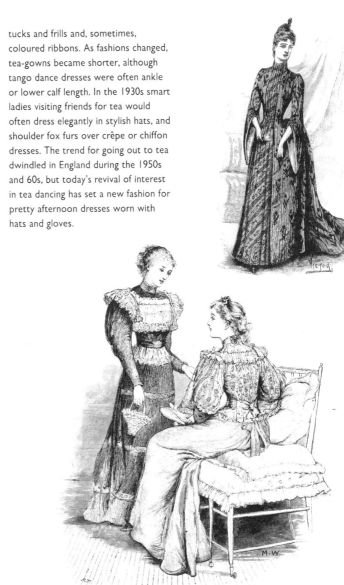

Tea-gown in gold brocade and lace over salmon-coloured voile.

The 30s were a time of elegant living for the wealthy who spent much of their time in fashionable resorts around the world. Their wardrobes contained a number of elegant dresses that were designed specially for afternoon tea in expensive hotels and tea salons.

TEA-TIME *on the* RIVIERA

MODELS *by* WORTH

Below

Let's away to another part of the world, where the sun shines on mimosa and almond blossoms. In the lounge of a well-known hotel looking out on the blue Mediterranean a group of charmingly dressed girls are waiting for tea.

In a corner of the room sits a girl in bottle-green crêpe satin—such a deep lovely shade of bottle green. She is wearing a coat of the satin over a dress of the same. The little coat has green, beaded plaques from the centre of which drop tassels. This is the only trimming other than the stitching, which finishes the slanting strappings on the bodice of the princess frock. Note the subtly dipped tunic skirt.

Above

One girl wears a black velvet skirt with a blouse of white chenille velvet embroidered with black chenille, the same embroidery being used to edge the skirt. Beside her is a navy-blue crêpe-de-Chine, trimmed ingeniously with little red tassels. Can you see that they edge the scalloped hem of the skirt, which is cut to the accepted dipping line behind?

The name "Orange Pekoe" has nothing to do with flavour, and everything to do with leaf size, but connoisseurs recognize that the large leaves denoted by the name will almost certainly yield a fragrant, high quality tea. The taste of different teas is affected by seasonal changes in the weather, and for consistency teas are blended.

SPECIAL BLENDS

When tea has been processed it is carefully graded according to leaf size and appearance. The two main grades are "leaf" and "broken leaf". The leaf grades for large leaves are called Orange Pekoe, Pekoe and Pekoe Souchong. Broken grades include Broken Orange Pekoe, Broken Pekoe and Broken Pekoe Souchong. The name "Pekoe" comes from the Chinese Amoy dialect word *pek-ho*, meaning "white down", and refers to the downy tips of the young leaf buds. Small leaf teas are known as Fannings, and the smallest particles, the Dust, are valued for use in tea-bags as they give a strong, quickly brewed infusion. The broken grades give stronger, darker teas than leaf grades, the latter being noted for their flavour and fragrance.

Charles, the 2nd Earl Grey, is said to have been given the recipe for the tea that is named after him by a mandarin while on a diplomatic mission to China.

❧ SEPTEMBER ❧

3

4

5

6

7

8

9

TEA LOAF

INGREDIENTS

12 fl oz (350 ml) of strong cold tea
8 oz (225 g) of light or dark soft brown sugar
3 oz (75 g) of raisins
3 oz (75 g) of sultanas
3 oz (75 g) of currants
3 oz (75 g) of mixed candied peel
10 oz (275 g) of self-raising flour, sifted
2 teaspoonfuls of mixed spice
1 egg, beaten

Makes 1 × 2 lb (900 g) loaf

Put the tea, sugar, raisins, sultanas, currants and peel into a bowl and leave to soak overnight. The following day, heat the oven to gas 4, 350°F, 180°C. Grease and line a 2lb (900g) loaf tin. Add the flour, spice and beaten egg to the fruit and tea mixture and beat thoroughly to incorporate plenty of air. Turn into the prepared tin and bake for 1 hour 45 minutes until a skewer comes out clean. Remove from the oven and turn out on to a wire rack to cool. Serve sliced with butter and preserves. Store, wrapped in cling film, in an air-tight tin.

HOME-MADE CAKES

A great deal of the pleasure to be had from visiting a tea-shop is in the display of wickedly tempting cakes. For cooks who like to make their own tea-time treats but are hesitant about trying to produce anything quite as elaborate as those shown in the shop window, here is a recipe for a deliciously moist fruit loaf made with tea.

Many tea-shops find that their "home-made cakes" sell better than all the fancy gateaux and pastries. Today's trend is for healthy carrot cakes or wholesome oatcakes rather than the cream-filled indulgences that were once so popular.

TEA CAKES

Many people enjoy a toasted tea cake with their afternoon cup of tea. This is a round bun made from a light yeasted dough and flavoured with dried fruits. Traditionally, it is cut in half and toasted, and then spread liberally with butter and jam.

❧ S E P T E M B E R ❧

10
11
12
13
14
15
16

☙ SEPTEMBER ❧

17
18
19
20
21
22
23

TEA AT GUNTER'S

Gunter's of Berkeley Square was one of the more elegant and fashionable tea-rooms in London. It is immortalized in Pamela Haines' novel *Tea at Gunter's*, in which the magic memories of the past are inextricably entwined with a nostalgia for elegant afternoon teas. The heroine rather sadly writes: "Even in dreams (particularly in dreams), I never go back now. Gunter's is gone anyway. I was in London yesterday and, stupidly, looked for it . . . asking a man just turned out of Chesterfield Street: 'Gunter's? It's gone. Been gone years now. . . . A nice little teashop, Gunter's – people still ask after it. . . .'"

The menu included tea, coffee or chocolate at 1/- a pot, anchovy toast or toasted scones at 9d, a toasted bun, buttered toast or bread and butter for 6d, asparagus rolls at 4d each, sandwiches from 9d to 1/-, and various pastries, tartines, gateaux and sponge cakes, priced from 3d to 6d. It also offered ice cream soda at 1/6, fresh fruit salad and cream for 2/- and ices costing 9d, 1/-, 1/6 and 2/-.

Gunter's was a favourite haunt of fashionable Edwardian ladies and gentlemen, and of governesses and nannies from wealthy households treating their young charges to an afternoon outing.

AT TEA

In the early years of this century, country and seaside tea-gardens provided a welcome resting-place for those who had ventured out of the cities in cars and charabancs and on bicycles.

OUT TO TEA

Although the unsettled and unpredictable British weather has always made outdoor summer activities somewhat risky, taking tea in the open air is a very popular pastime. Tea-gardens in the country are as popular as tea-shops in the town, and certain summer events are closely associated with the idea of tea – a visit to Wimbledon is not complete without a strawberry tea, and Buckingham Palace garden parties, Henley Regatta, cricket matches, village fêtes and bazaars all have their tea tent or pavilion laid out ready with pots of tea, sandwiches and cakes.

❧ SEPTEMBER ❧

24	
25	
26	
27	
28	
29	
30	

OCTOBER

1	
2	
3	
4	
5	
6	
7	

UNDER LOCK AND KEY

The first caddies to be used in Europe were imported from China and Japan. These were square or hexagonal, usually made of red stoneware, and had caps that were used to measure the tea. As tea became more expensive, it needed to be closely guarded by the lady of the house and so was kept in a lockable caddy in the drawing-room. The caddy was now formed rather like a small chest and held two containers, for green and black teas, and a bowl which was either used for blending the teas or for storing sugar – another expensive commodity. Since caddies were to be on show in the main part of the house, they were often decoratively embellished with brass, gold or silver, or inlaid with mother of pearl, ivory, tortoiseshell or rare woods.

Caddy spoons are often made in the shape of a shell, or have a shell motif, because, in the early days, the Chinese very thoughtfully packed an empty scallop shell in the top of tea-chests, to be used for measuring the tea into the teapot. The spoons were also known as "cadee chells" or "cadee ladles".

Before 1820 caddies were usually fitted with brass or silver locks. By 1850 tea
was much cheaper and late Victorian caddies, like the one above, although still
decorative, were simpler and less expensive.

OCTOBER

8
9
10
11
12
13
14

THE MAD HATTER'S TEA PARTY
There was the table set out under a tree in front of the house, and the March Hare and the Hatter were having tea at it: a Dormouse was sitting between them, fast asleep, and the other two were using it as a cushion, resting their elbows on it, and talking over its head. "Very uncomfortable for the Dormouse," thought Alice: "only as it's asleep, I suppose it doesn't mind." The table was a large one, but the three were all crowded together at one corner of it: "No room! No room!" they cried out when they saw Alice coming. "There's plenty of room," said Alice indignantly, and she sat down in a large armchair at one end of the table. "Have some wine," the March Hare said in an encouraging tone. Alice looked all round the table, but there was nothing on it but tea. "I don't see any wine," she remarked. "There isn't any," said the March Hare. "Then it wasn't very civil of you to offer it," said Alice angrily. "It wasn't very civil of you to sit down without being invited," said the March Hare. "I didn't know it was your table," said Alice; "it's laid for a great many more than three."

From *Alice's Adventures in Wonderland* by Lewis Carroll.

"Take some more tea," the March Hare said to Alice, very earnestly. "I've had nothing yet," Alice replied in an offended tone, "so I can't take more."

A 21-piece Butterfly Wing tea-set in the "Mode" range sold in the 1930s for
about £2 8s 9d (£2.44). Today it is worth about £500.

THE DECORATIVE THIRTIES

The years between the wars are remembered as a golden age of elegant tea drinking, and new designs in china and silverware changed the look of the fashionable tea table. Clarice Cliff created masterpieces, using brilliant colours and the typical geometric shapes of the Art Deco movement for her "Fantasque" and "Biarritz" ranges, and many of the potteries used designs by leading contemporary artists such as Vanessa Bell, Duncan Grant and Paul Nash. Nash designed for Foley China, which later became part of Shelley Pottery. The Shelley family had been running a successful earthenware company since the eighteenth century, when their customers included Josiah Wedgwood. At the end of the nineteenth century the company produced Art Nouveau tea-sets in brilliantly coloured glazed earthenware, and their famous "Dainty White" with its fluted panels and scalloped edges. In the 1920s and 30s, their Art Deco tea services introduced bold, brightly coloured motifs typical of the period – sunbursts, peacock tails and the butterfly wing design shown here. Eric Slater created the innovative "Mode" and "Vogue" ranges with their characteristic conical cups and triangular handles. Other notable tea ware from the same period includes Susie Cooper's subtle designs in dusty pinks and pastel greens, teapots by Carlton Ware and novelty ware by James Sadler.

OCTOBER

| 15 |
| 16 |
| 17 |
| 18 |
| 19 |
| 20 |
| 21 |

OCTOBER

22	
23	
24	
25	
26	
27	
28	

THE CORNER SHOP

When tea first became available in Britain, it was sold by apothecaries and by general merchants who dealt in such things as hops, tobacco, spices and rum. As it became an established drink, tea and coffee merchants opened specialist shops to meet the demand. Until the 1820s the leaves were sold loose, and customers could buy as little or as much as they wanted in a screw of paper. The grocer would sell the tea "straight" or blended to the customer's requirements. In 1826 John Horniman introduced packet tea in an effort to encourage housewives to ask for his teas rather than buying just any loose leaf that the retailer happened to have. He offered unadulterated tea, hygienically protected and uniformly weighed, but his idea did not catch on until the late 1880s, when most companies switched to packaging. (Some companies plied their newly-packaged goods from a horse-drawn van.) The packaging was all done by hand until the end of the First World War, when a revolutionary machine was introduced that made the packets from a reel of paper and measured the tea into them.

The idea of tea-bags developed from the little silk bags that a New York tea merchant, Thomas Sullivan, used for sending samples of tea to his clients for them to try before making their regular purchase. The first bags were made from fine cloth or gauze in the 1920s.

Hudson Ewbanks Kearly, Viscount Davenport, set up the International Tea Company in 1880, after working for a short time for Tetleys. The company later merged with Ridgways.

OCT • NOV

29
30
31
1
2
3
4

THE PERFECT TEASHOP

Different people expect different things from a tea-shop, but there are certain features that are essential for every customer. Customers should not be expected to queue for self-service – they have come in to rest weary legs and recover from shopping or work, or just to escape from the world outside, and they should not have to stand for a further ten minutes while those in front try to decide between ham or cucumber sandwiches. Gentle, kind and polite waitresses should arrive at the table with their order pads and then deliver the requested refreshment with a smile. Tables should ideally be covered with clean, pretty cloths; failing that, the table-tops must be clean. Given that fine porcelain is impractical, the cups should at least be reasonably thin and easy to lift and hold. The menu should cater to all tastes – some vegetarian fillings in sandwiches, wholesome cakes as well as cream buns, dainty pastries and shortbreads as well as lavish gateaux. There must be a choice of tea – Indian and China, scented and flavoured teas, and herbal infusions – and milk and lemon should be readily available. Last but not least, the atmosphere is absolutely crucial – the room should be calm and peaceful, with perhaps some gentle music playing, preferably classical or tunes from the 20s and 30s that are reminiscent of the heyday of tea drinking.

No British seaside holiday is complete without several visits to the local tea-shops. On hot days a cup of tea is the best answer to summer thirst, and on wet days the shops also provide welcome shelter.

This very strange machine was presumably designed for commercial use in an establishment where the staff were either considered incapable of measuring tea with a spoon, or so untrustworthy that they might steal the tea.

A PERFECT BREW

Surprisingly, a cup of tea contains slightly more caffeine than a cup of coffee, but whereas the caffeine in coffee is released quickly into the body and affects the circulation by stimulating the heart, caffeine in tea is released slowly and has a direct effect on the central nervous system. It increases mental activity and makes the drinker more alert. Tannin slows down the effects of the caffeine, so that its benefits are noticeable for longer and reduce more gradually than the effects of coffee. This makes tea the perfect stimulant that revives and refreshes. To make a perfect cup of tea every time follow the golden rules:

- Fill the kettle with freshly-drawn cold water and bring to the boil.
- When it is nearly boiling, pour a little water into the teapot, swill round, then tip away.
- Put into the teapot one caddy spoonful of tea for each person and one for the pot.
- Take the pot to the boiling kettle and, without allowing the water to go off the boil, pour the water on to the leaves.
- Replace the teapot lid and leave to brew for a few minutes, remembering that small-leafed black teas take three or four minutes, and larger-leafed black teas, oolongs and green teas take a little longer.
- Pour the tea and add milk or lemon, or neither, according to taste.

NOVEMBER

5

6

7

8

9

10

11

WHETHER IN THE COUNTRY, OR DOWN
BY THE SEA—I KNOW OF NOTHING
BETTER THAN
A NICE CUP OF TEA!

THE TABLE IS SET

Afternoon tea parties for children are usually served at sturdy dining tables, whereas elegant drawing-room teas demand smaller side tables. The first tea tables were imported from the East Indies in the late 1600s, and English cabinet-makers soon started making rectangular, circular, octagonal and scalloped tables with a raised rim around the edge to prevent accidents. The tables stood about three feet high, and the tops were usually large enough to accommodate all the necessary tea equipage. Some were hinged, so that the top tilted against the wall when not in use. Smaller tables of similar design which stood about two feet high were placed beside armchairs to

GOD BLESS OUR 'LEVENSES!

A WISH FOR YOUR BIRTHDAY

WELCOME

SAY WOULDN'T IT BE LOVELY
I SAY WHAT A SPREE
IF I WON A LITTLE SWEEP
AND BROUGHT HIM HOME
TO TEA !!!

1st PRIZE

take guests' cups and saucers. These were called teapoys, although the word later came to mean a small table containing a built-in caddy with one, two or three compartments. These were usually made of walnut or mahogany, but some were porcelain or stoneware. Another type of small tea table was the kettle stand which held the silver kettle, its matching tripod and burner. These too had a raised rim around the edge, a metal lining to

protect the wood from the heat of the kettle, and sometimes a sliding shelf on which to place the teapot. Even the most modest of tea tables and stands were elegantly styled and delicately decorated with rococo and chinoiserie motifs. Most had stylishly curving cabriole legs, which ended in carved ball-and-claw feet, and the raised rims were latticed or pierced and often finished with pie-crust or scalloped edging.

The podgy, pink-cheeked toddlers in these pictures are typical of the work of Mabel Lucie Attwell. Her early work in the late 1890s was strongly influenced by the Art Nouveau movement, but after having her own children she developed these delightful chubby children who appeared on posters, calendars, greetings cards, advertisements and in children's books.

✹NOVEMBER✹

12

13

14

15

16

17

18

NOT OUR CUP OF TEA

While the British sip their tea at 4 o'clock in the afternoon, people in other countries enjoy theirs in other ways. The Tibetans will drink anything up to thirty or forty cups a day. They use brick tea from China, which is chipped into cold water and boiled for hours until very black. A little salt or soda is added and the liquor is strained into a cylinder. A piece of rancid yak butter is then stirred in, and the tea is drunk from little wooden bowls. The Eskimos boil leaves and water together in a kettle for ten minutes and serve it scalding hot before it turns to ice crystals. In Korea, tea-leaves are dropped into boiling water and then served with raw eggs and rice cakes. The Burmese consume "letpet" tea, which is made from green leaves, steamed and pressed into bamboo canes or deep pits, and left to pickle for several months. The fermented leaves are then washed in brine and eaten as a salad with garlic, oil and sometimes dried fish. Mongolians use brick tea which is boiled with water, salt and fat. The brew is then strained and mixed with butter, milk and flour. Arabs drink mint tea from glasses, as do Turks, who drink tea all day, served from little round trays hawked by boys in the streets, or in the numerous bars and cafés. Zulus drink their tea very sweet, in India and Pakistan the tea is boiled with milk, water, sugar and cardamom, and Russians drink theirs with jam.

The British are not alone in enjoying their afternoon cups of tea. America was once and is again becoming a tea-drinking nation. In Canada, tea made up an important part of early shipments of cargoes to the settlers, and New Zealand and Australia have always been avid tea drinkers.

SPARKLING TEA PUNCH

1 pint of freshly brewed China tea
2–3 oz (50–75 g) of demerara sugar
freshly squeezed juice of 1 orange and 1 lemon
1 glass of brandy
1 glass of curaçao
1 bottle of medium dry sparkling cider
a few strawberries, sliced

Strain the tea and mix with the sugar. Stir until the sugar is dissolved and then chill. To serve, add the orange and lemon juice, brandy and curaçao to the tea, pour in the chilled cider and add the sliced strawberries.

MINT TEA

2 sprigs of fresh mint
freshly squeezed juice of 1 orange and 2 lemons
2 cups of freshly brewed strong Ceylon tea
a large pinch of powdered ginger dissolved in a little hot water
1 cup of cold water
sugar to taste

Bruise the mint leaves and pour over the fruit juices and the strained tea. Add the dissolved ginger, sugar to taste and the cold water. Chill for at least an hour, then serve with ice.

CHASE & SANBORN'S
TEA Gives Life new Charm

Iced tea punches are wonderfully refreshing and make elegant and unusual cocktails for hot summer evenings.

TO MAKE TEA CAUDLE

Make a quart of strong green tea and pour out into a skillet, and set it over the fire; then beat the yolks of four eggs and mix with them a pint of white wine, a grated nutmeg, sugar to your taste, and put all together; stir it over the fire till 'tis very hot, then drink it in china dishes as caudle.

E. Smith's *Compleat Housewife*, 1736

THE ORIGINS OF ICED TEA

A favourite summer drink for all open-air occasions is iced tea. This was first introduced by an Englishman, Richard Blechynden, at the St Louis Fair in 1904. Because of the scorching weather he was unable to sell his hot tea, so he poured it over ice and immediately sold gallons.

❉NOVEMBER❉

19
20
21
22
23
24
25

26
27
28
29
30
1
2

A PRECIOUS COMMODITY

In the 1660s, when tea was a new and rare commodity, the price was high (ranging from 16 to 60 shillings) and only royalty and the aristocracy could afford to buy it. A few years after the herb became well known in Britain, Charles II imposed heavy tea taxes in order to fill the nation's coffers, and although the drink was popular, it was too expensive for most people to buy on the open market and so a healthy black market sprang up. In the 1670s a pound of tea cost anything from 5 to 25 shillings, London prices being the cheapest. Poor families bought very small amounts, an ounce or two at a time, and made it last by drinking it very weak. Some retailers advertised their teas as "strong and will endure the Change of Water three or four times". Prices stayed high until 1784, when the tax was reduced from 119% to $12\frac{1}{2}$%, but the East India Company's monopoly on the tea trade with China continued to keep the cost up. When this monopoly was broken in 1833, the market opened up to new brokers, and healthy competition set in. The change from selling tea loose to marketing it in named packets led to intense campaigning to secure regular customers, and prices were lowered when Gladstone reduced the Tea Tax from one shilling per pound in 1863 to sixpence in 1865 and fourpence in 1890. The tax fluctuated through the first half of this century, until all duties were abolished in 1964.

Two twentieth-century invoice headings and an 1878 invoice from Twinings, showing Darjeeling tea for the first time.

A.A. Thompson wrote: "They talk about Hitler's secret weapon, but what about England's secret weapon – tea. That's what keeps us going and that's what's going to carry us through . . . the Army, the Navy, the Women's Institute – what keeps 'em together is tea!"

THE GREAT MORALE BOOSTER

During the first two years of the First World War, tea did not suffer from any major upheavals, but in 1916 the activities of the German U-boats meant that supplies in Britain dwindled, queues lengthened and profiteering became evident. By late 1916, the price was up to almost three shillings a pound and the government ruled that 90% of tea must be price controlled. By February 1918, all tea was National Control Tea and retailed at a fixed 2s 8d. Four months before the 1918 armistice, rationing was introduced, but there was never a shortage.

At the beginning of the Second World War, tea stocks were dispersed in case of invasion or bombing, and by September 1939 thirty thousand tons of tea had been removed from London to a variety of hiding-places. In 1940 tea was rationed, along with bacon, butter, sugar and meat. The allowance was two ounces per person per week, and batches of coupons were often handed to grocers and tea merchants who maintained the family's regular supply. Many people saw tea as a real life-saver – troops brewed up as soon as they halted their manoeuvres, the Women's Institute dished out cups of tea after air raids, and many found comfort in a shared pot at times of extreme hardship.

DECEMBER

3

4

5

6

7

8

9

❈ DECEMBER ❈

10

11

12

13

14

15

16

INFUSIONS AND TISANES

The word tea should only be applied to the beverage made with the leaves of the Camellia Sinensis. Other brews are usually referred to as herbal infusions or tisanes. A large number of these have recognized medicinal properties and are available in health food shops as well as from tea merchants. The drinking of healthy herbal brews has a long history – the word tisane deriving from the Greek *ptisane*, which referred to a drink made from barley. As far back as the early nineteenth century a mixture of leaves from British hedgerows and shrubs was being marketed as "British Tea", although this was more an effort to beat the high cost of tea and cash in on a healthy black market trade than to promote herbal drinks. The following are the most commonly used herbs:

- **comfrey** is good for coughs
- **dandelion** cleans the blood and has diuretic powers
- **elderflower** soothes the nerves and is good for gout
- **ginseng** is claimed to have remarkable powers of brightening the eyes, invigorating the body, prolonging life and as a remedy for impotence
- **hibiscus** is rich in vitamin C
- **lime (or linden) flower**, very popular in France, eases headaches and induces sleep
- **peppermint** is excellent for indigestion

Crabtree and Evelyn's range of five herbal infusions includes rosehip, which is drunk for its delicate flavour, and camomile, which is excellent for inducing sleep as well as for inflammations and toothache.

POTS OF STYLE

Since Chinese teapots arrived in Europe in the mid seventeenth century, pots of all shapes and sizes have been created by European potters and silversmiths. Silver teapots were not manufactured in any great number until Queen Anne's reign. The first British ceramic pots appeared in the 1740s and followed the Oriental trend for unusual shapes, with many of the Staffordshire potteries producing salt-glaze pots in the form of squirrels, camels, birds, vegetables, fruits, houses, hearts and even ships. Some pots were made with two separate compartments and two spouts, one for black tea and one for green, since it was fashionable to offer both to guests.

This vast Twinings teapot was made for the Great International Exhibition in 1851 and holds thirteen and a half gallons, approximately 1220 cups of tea. It stands two and a half feet high and has a girth of six feet.

❇DECEMBER❇

| 17 |
| 18 |
| 19 |
| 20 |
| 21 |
| 22 |
| 23 |

❈ D E C E M B E R ❈

24
25
26
27
28
29
30

THE THINGS PEOPLE SAY

During our ascent of Mount Everest tea constantly gave us cheer and vigour.

Sir Edmund Hilary

Surely every one is aware of the divine pleasures which attend a wintry fireside: candles at four o'clock, warm hearthrugs, tea, a fair tea-maker, shutters closed, curtains flowing in ample draperies to the floor, whilst the wind and rain are raging audibly without.

From *Confessions of an English Opium-Eater*
Thomas De Quincy

If you are cold, tea will warm you –
If you are heated, it will cool you –
If you are depressed, it will cheer you –
If you are excited, it will calm you.

W.E. Gladstone

There is s subtle charm in the taste of tea which makes it irresistible and capable of idealization. . . . It has not the arrogance of wine, the self-consciousness of coffee, nor the simpering innocence of cocoa.

From *The Book of Tea*
Okakura Kakuzo

Fairyland Pictures

ERNEST·NISTER·LONDON   Nº 4666   E·P·DUTTON & Cº NEW YORK

In winter or in summer, indoors or out, freshly-brewed tea makes the perfect
drink to revive and refresh.

EVERYTHING STOPS FOR TEA

Since the early 1980s a new interest in tea has been evident in Europe and America. In France and Germany, traditionally coffee-drinking countries, new tea-shops have opened, and established ones have seen an increase in business. In the United States, enterprising tea-shop owners are even making their own clotted cream to serve with scones in their newly-opened establishments, while in Britain tea-shops have opened in unlikely places and quickly become very popular, several books of tea-time recipes have appeared on bookshop shelves, and the ritual of going out to tea has once again become very fashionable. Tea-dances are now regularly held, not only in the grander hotels and restaurants, but in village halls and provincial social centres. Tourists make sure that they visit the better-known venues around Britain for a full afternoon tea or a cream tea with scones and clotted cream.

◪DEC ◆ JAN◩

31

1

2

3

4

5

6

ACKNOWLEDGEMENTS

Please note that as there are no page numbers, the date at the top of the first page is given as the reference point.

The author and publisher would like to thank the following for permission to reproduce the illustrations and photographs in this book. Particular thanks go to Sam Twining, OBE and his assistant, Wyn Harvey, for their valuable time and free use of the Twining archives. Thanks are also due to Martin Trelawny for the special photography, and to Pam Taylor for the loan of her china.

Picture sources:

Bodleian Library, Oxford: Garraway's Coffee House, Jan 15; Fine Hyson, March 5; Map of Ceylon, June 18; Chinese Tales, overleaf from July 2; Terrabona Card, July 23. *Bridgeman Art Library:* Tea Trade in China, George Chinnery, Jan 1; Coffee House, Jan 22; Tea Party, Nicolaes Verkolje, Jan 29; Chinese School, Feb 5; Taking Tea at the White House, London Museum, overleaf from Feb 5; A Family at Tea, Victoria and Albert Museum, Feb 12; Octagonal bowl and saucer, Feb 12; Cow creamer, J. Shrubsole Ltd, Feb 19; Château de Versailles, Ollivier, Mar 26; Worcester porcelain, Bonhams, April 2; Edo Tea House, Victoria and Albert Museum, April 9; The Tea Party, Vittoria Reggianini, Christie's, London, April 16; Tea Leaves, Alma Broadbridge, City of York Art Gallery, June 4; Early 20s tea gown, White House Catalogue, overleaf from Aug 27; Tea at Gunters, John Strickland Goodall, Sept 17; Alice in Wonderland, British Library, Oct 8; Tea on the Pier, Robert Tyndall, Oct 29; Summer Afternoon Tea, Thomas Barrett, Phillips Auctioneers, Nov 12; La Table Blanche, Phillips Auctioneers, Dec 17; The Round Pond, Wolverhampton Art Gallery, Dec 31. *British Museum:* Catlap for Ever, March 12; *Mary Evans Picture Library:* A Tea Garden, overleaf from Feb 5; Clippers off Valparaiso, April 30; Cullen's Tea, June 25; ABC Cafe, July 2; The Children's Tea, Helen Allingham, Aug 20; Tango in France, Aug 27; Tango insert, Aug 27; Tea gowns, 1889, 1893 and 1926, overleaf from Aug 27; Confectioner's shop, Sept 10; Parrot, Sept 24; Corner shop, Oct 22; Tea measuring machine, Nov 5. *Crabtree & Evelyn Ltd:* Herbal brews, Tessa Traeger, Dec 10; *Fine Art Photographic Library Ltd:* A Sunday Afternoon, May 28; Dolls' Tea Party, July 16; Tea Party in the Garden, August 6; Teetotallers, Oct 1. *Rank Hovis Ltd:* Sandwiches, July 9. *The Hulton-Deutsch Collection:* Boston Tea Party, Mar 19. *Illustrated London News Picture Library:* Unloading at docks, May 7. *National Maritime Museum, Greenwich:* Emma Hamilton, overleaf from Feb 5; *Priory Gallery, Bishops Cleeve, Cheltenham, Glouc:* Afternoon Tea, William Henry Margetson, cover picture. All the other photographs and illustrations in this book are courtesy of Sam Twining, OBE and the author.

Conversion of Measurements for American and Metric Equivalents:

MADEIRA CAKE (May 14)
6 oz/$\frac{3}{4}$ cup/175 g sugar
6 oz/1$\frac{1}{4}$ cups/175 g flour
4 oz/$\frac{1}{2}$ cup/100 g butter
sprinkle with superfine sugar

TEA LOAF (Sept 10)
12 fl oz/1$\frac{1}{2}$ cups/350 ml of strong cold tea
8 oz/1$\frac{1}{4}$ cups/225 g light or dark brown sugar
3 oz/just under $\frac{1}{2}$ cup/75 g raisins/sultanas/currants/mixed candied peel
10 oz/2$\frac{1}{4}$ cups/275 g self-raising flour, sifted

SPARKLING TEA PUNCH (Nov 19)
1 pint/2$\frac{1}{2}$ cups/600 ml China tea
2–3 oz/$\frac{1}{2}$–$\frac{2}{3}$ cup/50–75 g demerara (turbinado or light brown) sugar
7–8 fl oz/1 cup/200–225 ml curaçao/brandy
1$\frac{3}{4}$ pint/4$\frac{1}{4}$ cups/1000 ml cider (alcoholic)

MINT TEA (Nov 19)
1 pint/2–2$\frac{1}{2}$ cups/600 ml China tea
7–8 fl oz/1 cup/200–225 ml cold water

TEA CAUDLE (Nov 19)
1 qt/5 cups/1200 ml strong green tea
1 pint/2$\frac{1}{2}$ cups/600 ml white wine